We dedicate
this book to all those children
who have experienced divorce
(or serious splits) in their lives.

A special thanks to my husband for his
graphic design eye and his patience.

A special thanks to Fanie, Cari
and Sheela for their thoughts.

IAmSethEliot.com
Smile From The Inside, Inc.

Glossary

Here are definitions of the big words:

A "**Behavioral Therapist**" is someone who helps you feel better about yourself and other people. They help you get along better with friends and family. They teach you how to act when things get tough.

A "**Smileologist**" helps connect kids to their pain, move through their emotions/wounds, and helps to find their smile again.

"**Grief**" is a strong and sometimes overwhelming emotion that comes after a terrible, no good event or experience.

"**The Hurt**" is the feeling that gathers in the pit of your stomach when you've been sad or experiencing lots of emotions.

"**Self-care**" skills are the every day tasks we do to ensure **WE** are our number #1 priority, safe, happy, at peace, and that all of our needs are met before we help anyone else with their needs, wants, or desires.

Dear Reader

Scout & The Serious Split tells the story of how two sisters navigate through a challenging experience when their loving and devoted parents decide to go their separate ways.

This book is designed for your edutainment. In other words, this story is meant to be both educational and entertaining.

Pay special attention to Scout's emotions, feelings, and behaviors as she deals with this challenging time in her life.

Afterwards, please use the last page OR you can visit our kid-friendly website where you will be prompted with questions and guides to discuss the various events and steps we all adventure through when faced with major obstacles in your own life.

Hopefully, Scout's story will help you the next time you experience a significant hurt, obstacle, experience, or loss.

The S.M.I.L.E. Adventure

Contents

Once upon a time,
In a suburb by the sea;
Lived my wonderful family,
Ima, Mum, Addie and me.

I'm Scout, just nearly ten,
Addie, well within her fours;
Come closer I have a story,
Before we giggle and play outdoors.

The first 6 years were fabulous,
Some might even say bliss;
But, soon after Addie was born,
Something went amiss.

Mum and Ima began acting like strangers,
With more and more arguments and fights;
Sometimes, I felt sad for Addie,
Because she missed their funny love bites.

Mum and Ima were often hurting,
They thought they hid it so well;
I love when we escaped to Bubbie's,
Finding magic through an enchanted spell.

They tried absolutely everything,
Day in and day out;
Read books, tried counseling,
They could not find their 'right' route.

They were just plain miserable,
A storm they could not weather;
Some Mums and Imas,
Are just not meant to stay together.

It would get loads better,
And then much much worse;
Tried giving each other 'space',
But that backfired like a curse.

They definitely tried their best,
Sometimes it's just not meant to be;
They were my two most favorite people,
So, what happens to Addie and me?

Ugh, the dreaded word divorce,
A picnic table has never seen so much stress;
They said they loved us... gingerly,
At that point, my life felt like a mess.

10

The next few weeks were ugly,
Brutal, even, in front of the judge;
He doesn't know my family at all...
My insides felt like sludge.

I guess I wasn't shocked,
I just truly never believed;
Addie cried a bit on my lap,
If I'm honest, I felt quite relieved.

The first few months were confusing,
We just barely got by;
Juggling between two houses,
Was nasty, I'm not gonna lie!

It was around six months later,
When I started to feel a bit strang
With tons of scary dreams,
This was a tremendous change.

One day I'd feel fine,
The next day not so much;
The good, the bad, and the ugly,
Girl, was I out of touch...?

Mum would say one thing to us,
Ima would say the opposite;
We were usually stuck in the middle
And on and on went the serious spl

I had to grow up real quick,
d take care of sweet little Adelyne;
Caught between Mum & Ima,
_ife was NOT a bowl of sunshine.

About one year later...
My parents started to be less trouble;
But it was I who started,
To feel all my emotions bubble.

Some silly boy at school...
Said something which really upset me;
(I've learned it's called a "trigger"),
And so I pushed him against a tree.

The school sent me home...
Neither parent knew what to do;
They immediately put me in therapy,
Something about behavioral, but I had no clue!

16

My first therapist was a little scary,
A suggestion from the school;
I didn't like the way he spoke,
He talked down to me, so uncool.

My second therapist was way too out there,
A middle-aged woman who worked with my Mum;
We did **NOT** understand each other,
At least she fed me candies, that was kinda yum.

When we had all but given up hope,
Ima knew this smileologist for a while;
He helped kids connect to their pain,
To move past it and find their smile.

He had way too many piercings,
And smelled like the good type of cheese;
But from the moment we first met,
I felt perfectly at ease.

18

This guy, wow, he really got me,
Sometimes better than me, myself, or I;
His parents got divorced when he was young,
So, he always connected with my "why".

I'll say I was quite impressed,
By his funny and wonderful wit;
Did I mention he had really yummy cookies?
And the comfiest couch, I must admit!

Today, he called me out on my "hurt,"
In the very deep pit of my belly;
Why was everyone else okay?
Was I the only one who felt like jelly?

I felt exposed and vulnerable,
And sad beyond belief;
Our beautiful family was gone,
And now I was drowning in grief.

Today I cried a little,
As we discussed my family's shift;
Deep down I want everyone to be happy,
For Addie and me, it would be a gift!

Afterward, Mum wiped away my tears,
And hugged me for a very long time;
Then, Ima and I hiked a mountain,
Holding hands in silence, **TOTALLY** worth the climb!

Today, I cried a lot!
I felt so much better after;
These emotions are definitely bonkers,
And then easily turn to laughter.

My coach said it was a release,
I've been holding onto far too long;
He said emotions come in waves,
And with grief, there's no right or wrong.

In time, I've learned that sometimes,
It's OK not to be ok;
I need to feel all my emotions,
Not shoo them all away.

I need to express my emotions,
Ask others for help and assistance, too;
'Cause there's no wrong way to handle this,
Just better ways to push through.

It's okay that Mum and Ima aren't together,
We will all move on with grace;
I've learned to give it time.
To be patient, loving, and to embrace.

I've learned to ask for support,
For the things that I feel I need;
Not like a new pony or bike,
Although t'would be AWESOME to have a trusted steed.

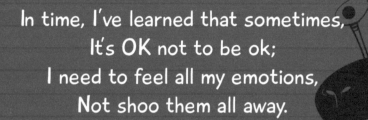

I now know this is not my fault,
My parents love me unconditionally;
I was getting used to our new normal and then,
Ima kissed someone else, and I wanted to flee.

I cringed at first,
Then, got a little mad;
But I want them BOTH to be happy,
My coach said it's okay to be sad.

I get to feel all my feelings,
I get to honor all of them with pride;
I get to have my own process,
To move through toward peace inside.

Mum got a brand new house,
Haven't seen her smile so much and jest;
I kinda miss our old one though,
But realize it's probably for the best.

When one door closes and shuts,
A window opens, breathing some fresh air;
Endings turn into new beginnings,
Which pave the way for lots of self-care!

I know the SMILE "adventure" is not over,
But I'm getting there more each day;
In life, we take two giant steps forward,
Followed by one tiny step back, I'd say...

Addie had a tough time this week,
So I sat down with her, holding her hand;
Seized my big sister moment saying,
We all have good days and bad, and I understand.

Healing is not a step-by-step process,
Sometimes it takes all your might;
To move upward and onward,
Knowing life will be better than alright!

We are all works in progress,
I have so much more to learn;
The more tools, the more confident I feel,
To enable the fire within to burn.

I don't need to have all the answers,
I don't need to have it all figured out;
Whatever life throws ahead of me,
I will handle it with grace, no doubt.

I'm not quite grateful yet,
And it's about so much more than me;
Bravery, courage, emotions,
And the truth shall set us free!

In loss, there's no right or wrong,
Through this entire challenge, I hope you see;
It was an incredible opportunity,
To recreate and discover a new(er) me.

Talk to your kids

Use these prompts to guide discussions about the various events we all adventure through when faced with major loss and/or obstacles in life.

Hopefully, Scout's story and the S.M.I.L.E. steps will help you re-discover your inner smile.

For a comprehensive guide to help discussions with your family, please visit: ScoutandtheSeriousSplit.com

S

SHOCK
Nature's first line of defense to protect the mind, body, and soul.
  a) Ask them how they are doing and what they are feeling
  b) Share how YOU are doing and what YOU are experiencing

m

MOCK-CCEPTANCE
The pause between the painful event AND the pain itself.
  a) Talk about what's happening now
  b) Tell them it's okay to feel anything and everything these days

i

IN-OVERWHELMDOM
Frustration. Anger. Sadness. Tears of Laughter. Significant emotions.
  a) Encourage them to share their thoughts and feelings with you
  b) Share YOUR thoughts and feelings with them
  c) Acknowledge & validate - be kind, patient, honest and transparent
  d) Ask them to share when they're feeling icky and YOU do the same
  e) Assure them we will all get through this

L

LEARNING
Now you know better, so you will do better!
  a) Ask them what they've learned thus far
  b) Share what YOU've learned thus far
  c) Discuss changes in families, school, present, and future
  d) Assure them everything will be better in the new normal

EMBRACE
Accept what has happened with grace, strength, and dignity.
  a) Inspire them to be creative and express themselves
  b) Lead by example and be the vision you wish to create

Author

Seth Eliot Santoro, CEC is also the author of "Smile From The Inside," "From Grief to Grace," and the first book in this Smile Adventure series and international bestseller, "Finn & The Ferocious Flu."

When he's not working on books, Seth helps kids, families, and adults heal and navigate stressful times and big changes in their lives.

His vision is to inspire the world to heal and find happiness.

Seth loves chocolate, chicken, and corn on the cob. He likes to eat lots of colorful fruits and veggies and he LOVES playing with his niece and nephew.

Seth Eliot Santoro

Robert Dersley

Artist

Robert draws all the time – he drew the doctor that delivered him, he drew his parents, his teachers and everyone else he knows.

He draws at work, at home, in the car (not recommended) and now he can say he's drawn a children's book too!

Printed in the USA
CPSIA information can be obtained
at www.ICGtesting.com
LVHW061921081123

763364LV00021B/251